LOVE TO RACE

Written by Amber Sawyer
Illustrated by Tami Joe DeLisle

Love to Race

Writen by Amber Sawyer

Story Illustrations by Tami Joe DeLisle

Dedication Illustration by Chloe Ochoa

Original Edit by Maria Carter

Edited by Marla McKenna

Proofread by Lyda Rose Haerle

Layout by Michael Nicloy

Author Photo by Mike Ferrell, Jr.

Digital Imaging of Original StoryIllustrations by Keith Glasgow, www.glasgowphoto.com

Original Photos for Story Illustrations by Marilyn Therrian and Peter Kilby

ISBN: 978-1945907678

Published by

NICO 11 PUBLISHING & DESIGN

MUKWONAGO, WISCONSIN

www.nico11publishing.com

Quantity order requests can be emailed to:

mike@nico11publishing.com

Printed in The United States of America

Every girl dreams of having a horse.

This book is dedicated to my dad, who always made sure his little girl never went a day without a horse in her life.

A special thank you to Peter Kass. Without you, this story would never have happened.

To my friend Lauren Grabowlski, you are always in my thoughts. May you rest in peace, my dear friend.

My name is Derek Bromac N.

My name ends with the letter N because I was born a long way from where I am now, in New Zealand.

How did I get to where I am now? Well, that's a pretty good story, and I'd love to tell it to you.

I was born in 2000 at a place called Bromac Farms. The owners there raised baby racehorses. When I was only 2 years old, I got to start racing!!

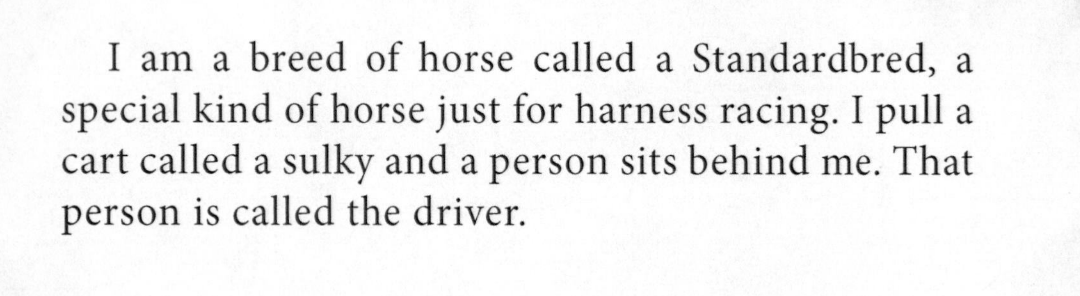

I am a breed of horse called a Standardbred, a special kind of horse just for harness racing. I pull a cart called a sulky and a person sits behind me. That person is called the driver.

I raced so well in New Zealand that I was sold to a person in California. One day, I got on an airplane with some of my friends from Bromac Farms, and we flew to the United States. Not many horses can say they've been on an airplane, but I HAVE!! I started winning lots of races in California.

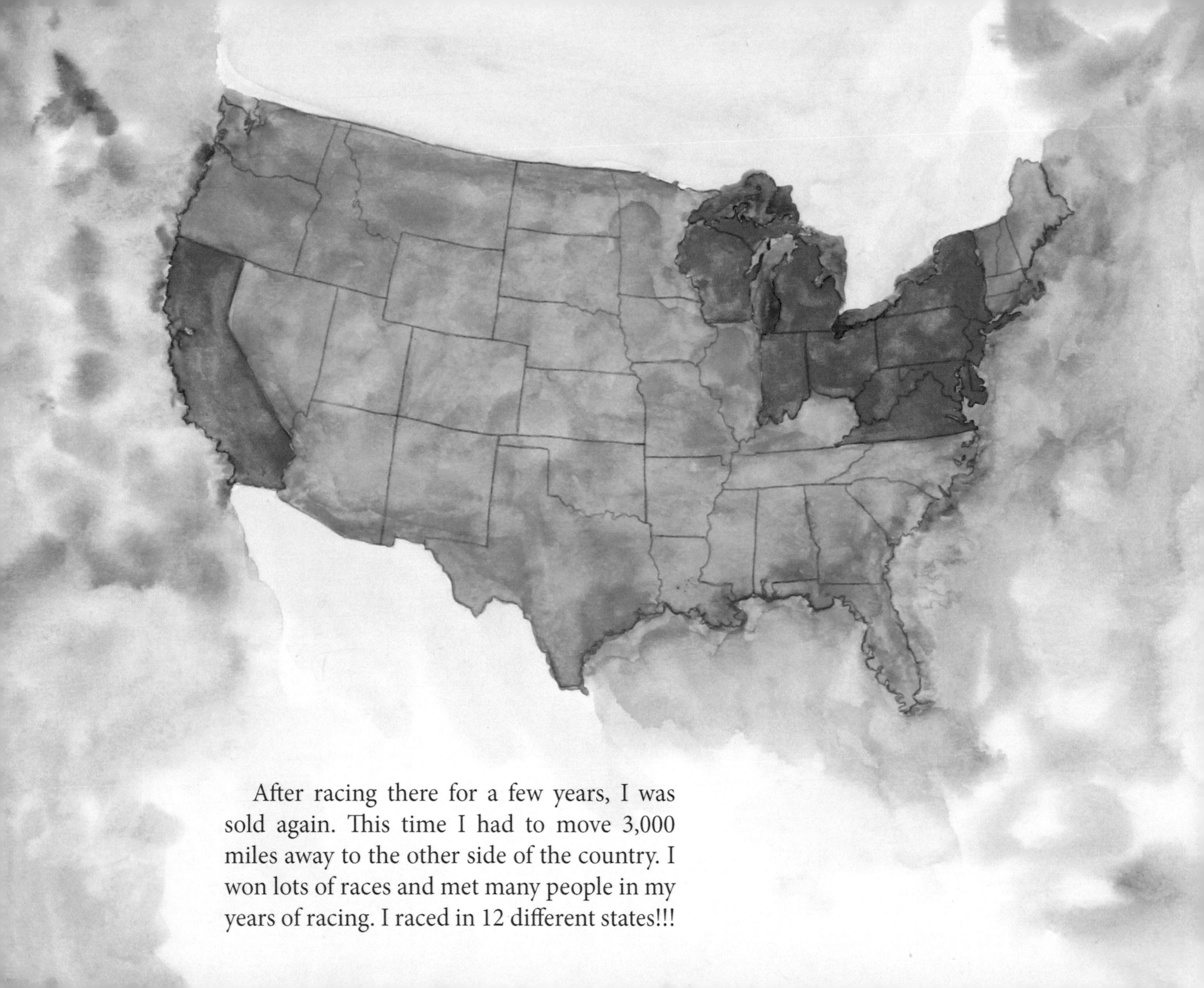

After racing there for a few years, I was sold again. This time I had to move 3,000 miles away to the other side of the country. I won lots of races and met many people in my years of racing. I raced in 12 different states!!!

When I was 13 years old, I met a very special person. His name was Peter, and we lived in Ohio. He loved me very much and took really good care of me, but one day something bad happened.

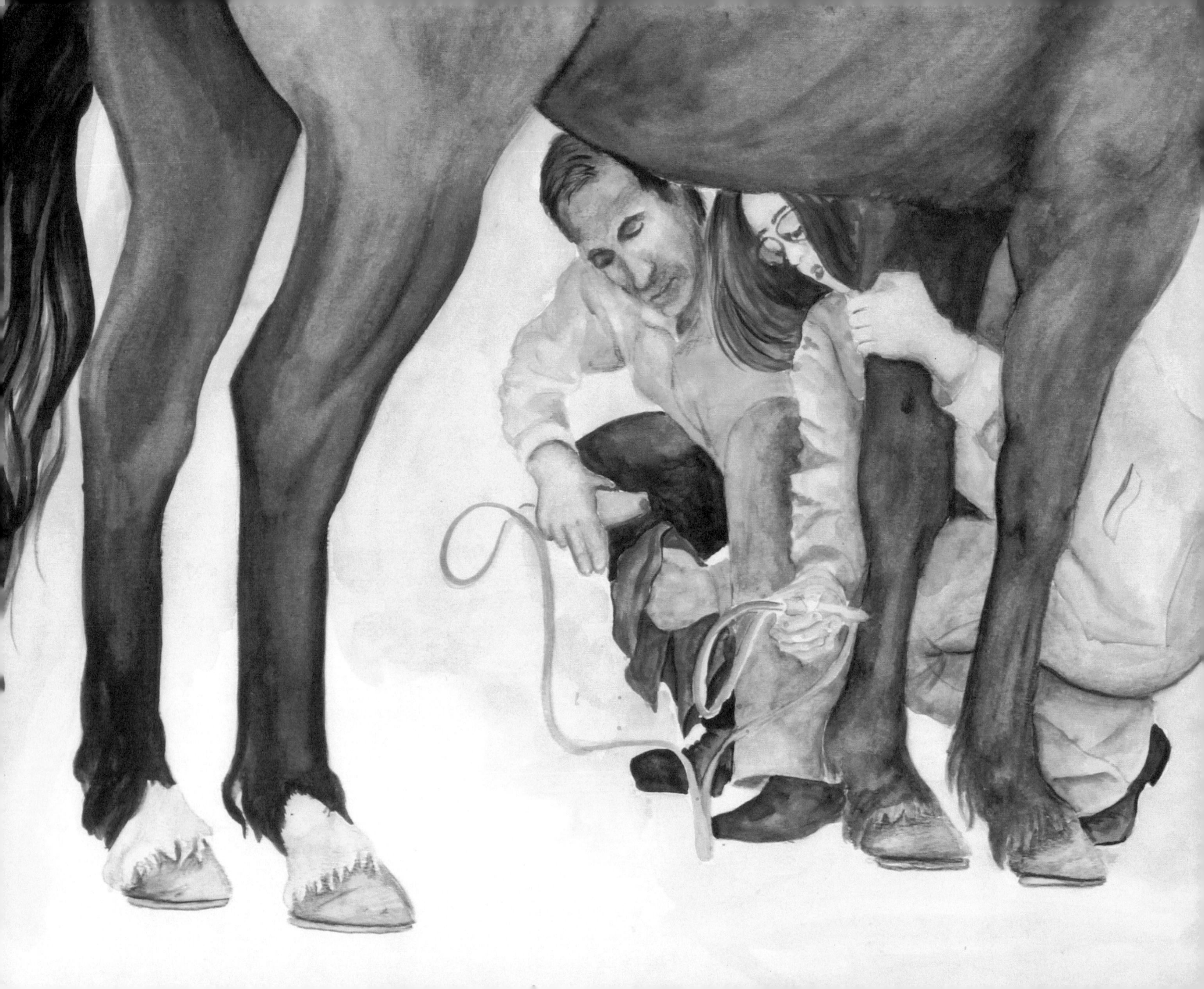

I was racing, and the race was almost over. All of a sudden, my front leg started to hurt. It was so painful for me as I limped off the racetrack. As soon as I got back to the barn, Peter and a veterinarian looked at my leg. There was bad news!! He said that I would probably never be able to race again!

Thirteen years old is pretty old for a racehorse, but I loved racing so much. I was so sad! Where would I go? What would I do? And most importantly, would I ever be able to race again?

My friend Peter wanted to find someone who would give me a great home and take the time to try and fix my leg so I could get back to doing what I loved most—being a racehorse! I would have to rest for a very long time, but I didn't care because I loved racing so much!

Peter told me that I was going to live in Wisconsin with a little boy named Paul and his mom and grandpa. Paul was going to be my new owner. I have had a lot of different people who owned me, but this was very different. You see, I was 13, and Paul was only 8! I was Paul's first horse, and he was going to help his mom fix my leg.

Oh, how I hoped they could!

It took almost a year for my leg to get better. Finally, I got in a horse trailer and was taken to my first race in over a year and a half. I was so excited but very nervous. Would I do any good? Would my leg be okay? Would I be able to beat any horses? Now I was 14 years old. All the horses in my race were so much younger than me. Not many horses my age are still racing.

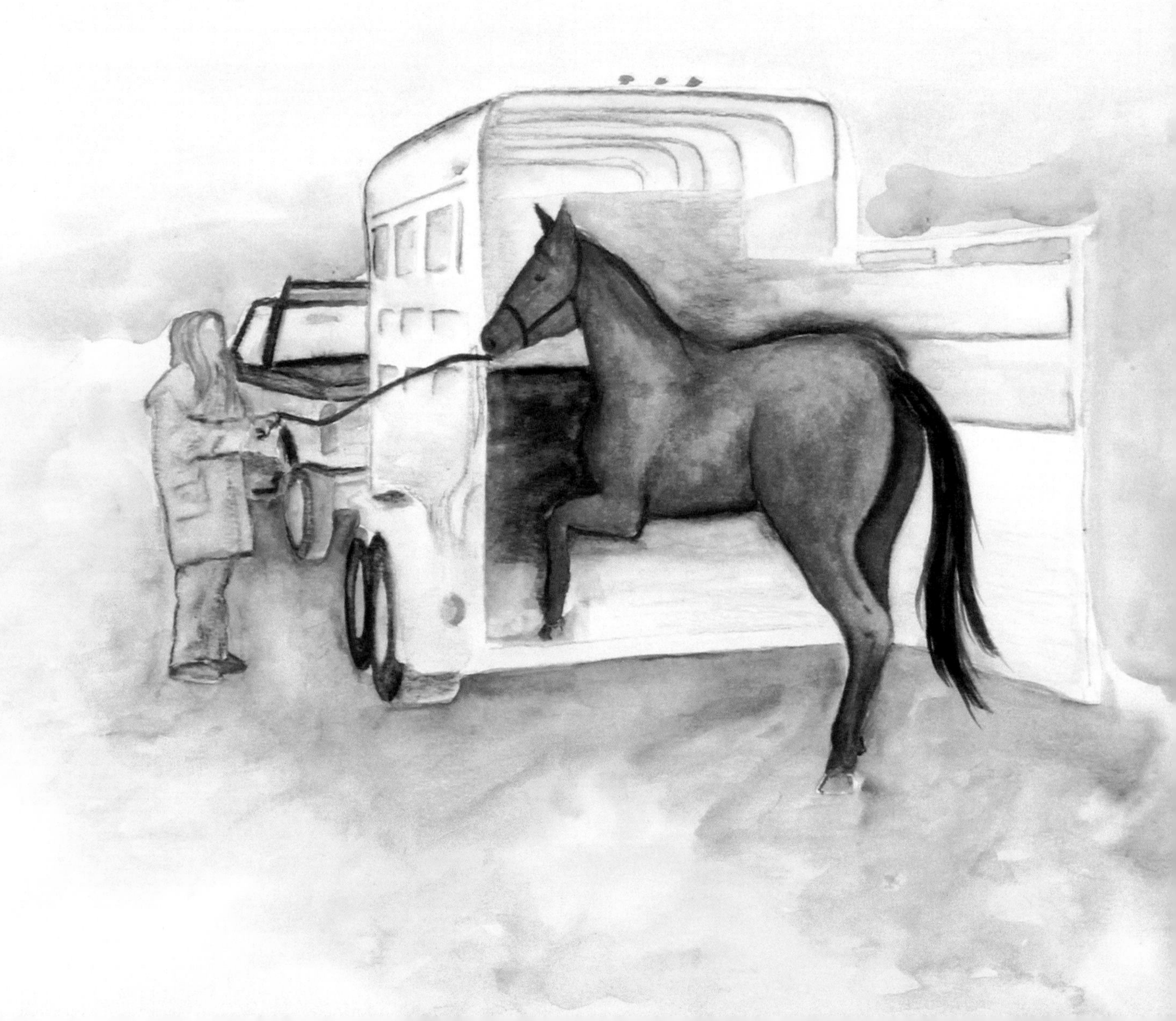

Before I knew it, we were at the racetrack, but this one wasn't like any track I had ever been to before! There were Ferris wheels, rides, games, balloons, and people everywhere! Paul could tell I was nervous, so he came over to pet me and said we were at a county fair. I had never seen one before!

All my other races had been very serious, with professional drivers and people coming in to bet on me, but as I waited for my turn to race, little kids from the fair kept coming up to pet me. They were wishing me good luck and giving me treats. Everyone was smiling and laughing and having a great time, and Paul's mom was going to drive me in the race. I wasn't nervous anymore! I could smell all the wonderful smells of cotton candy and corn dogs from the midway. I loved my new life! This was fun! Now I was going to try even harder in that race, so I could get to go to another county fair! I wanted to make Paul proud of me and show the veterinarian that I COULD race again! And guess what?

I finished third in my race that day.

Paul gave me hugs and lots of carrots after the race was over. It felt so good to be a racehorse again.

I traveled to lots of county fairs that summer with Paul and his family. I made lots of new friends at the races, and I loved to listen to them cheer for me in the grandstand while I raced.

Summer ended and when winter began I was able to rest.

The next summer arrived, and I looked forward to more county fairs. Now I was 15 years old. Not many horses can still race at my age. In fact, I was one of the oldest racehorses in the whole country! I knew I would have to work even harder this summer because all the horses would be so much younger than me. Off to the races we went, with Paul by my side.

One day, after a very long trailer ride, we pulled up to a county fair that was a long way from home in Northern Michigan. My good friend, Mr. Magee, was going to drive me that day. It had been a very long summer, and I was getting tired. All the other horses in my race were half my age or even younger!

We started the race, and I was in third place by the time the race was half over. I was so tired that I was ready to give up. My legs hurt and every muscle in my body ached. I didn't think I could go on.

I glanced over and saw Paul in the grandstand cheering his hardest for me. I hadn't won a race for him all summer. I knew I had to win this race for him. At my age, I didn't know how many more times I would be able to race. So, I gave it everything I had and I passed all those horses coming down the stretch. As I crossed the finish line, everyone in the grandstand was on their feet cheering for me. I heard the announcer say, "You are witnessing history, folks! This is Derek Bromac N, the oldest winning racehorse in the entire country!"

I was so happy! Me! Derek Bromac N, the horse that was never supposed to race again! A winner!

That was my very last win, and I will remember it forever. After a few more county fairs, I decided to retire from racing. I had raced for 13 years. I won 28 out of the 288 races I had been in. That's a lot! My travels took me to 2 counties, 12 different states, and 28 different racetracks. Not many horses have traveled as far as I have.

Even though I wasn't racing anymore, I still had plenty of work to do. Paul had so much to learn, and I had so much to teach him. I even taught him to crawl on my back and take me for a ride!

Every year, I get to go to the Midwest Horse Fair in Madison, Wisconsin, and teach thousands of people about Standardbreds and harness racing!

I have told my story to so many people. I have been in parades, schools, nursing homes, and I have even been on TV! I have so many more people to teach and lots of friends to make. Maybe someday I'll get to meet you too!

288 races—32 wins—28 racetracks—12 states—2 countries

Derek Bromac N was born in New Zealand, at Bromac Farms, in November of 2000. The son of Holmes Hanover and Desibo has a bankroll of $265,864 in 274 starts, with 32 wins. After racing in New Zealand as a 2-, 3-, and 4-year-old, Derek was shipped to California to begin his racing career in the United States. He immediately began dominating his competition at remarkable race times, once with only three shoes! This classy bay gelding found success wherever his travels took him and was often a barn favorite. His crazy antics of always sticking his tongue out while being harnessed, and on the racetrack, made him a horse that wouldn't easily be forgotten.

From California to New Jersey, and every racetrack in between, he was driven by some of the most elite and talented in the harness racing business. He was always known as the horse that always "gave his all."

In July of 2013, a very severe tear to his suspensory ligament (at age 13) was nearly the end for him. "The vet's suggestion was to put him down," former owner Peter Kass said. "He said Derek would never set foot on a racetrack again. I didn't believe it, and I wouldn't have it." Derek finished 2nd in the race that day, obviously racing on nothing but heart.

Competition was steep at Northfield Park, in Ohio, where Kass was stabled. With a yearlong recovery ahead, he opted to send the horse to his longtime friend, Amber Sawyer at Sawyer's Stables in Burnett, Wisconsin. Derek's gentle nature would make him the perfect first horse for Amber's 8-year-old son, Paul.

Wisconsin's cold temperatures and deep snow were the perfect remedy to slowly heal the torn suspensory on Derek's front leg. He was getting stronger every day, and by late March of 2014, he was ready to start back with his training. That June, with a solid foundation under him, he headed to the track for his first race in almost a year. The pari-mutuel track-life was just a memory for Derek; there were no more tote boards full of wagers; no more eager race fans with betting tickets in their hands; no more bright lights and perfectly groomed racetracks. Now there were Ferris wheels; hot dog stands; and children, with sticky faces full of cotton candy, cheering in the grandstands, waving to the old horse as he paraded past the midway of the county fair and took his place behind the starting gate. The déjà vu of a former headline written about him ten years prior read, "Derek Bromac N is Back, Baby!" as it was as true then as it was that day as Derek finished a strong third. The 14-year-old horse proved that he had more than enough in the tank to keep competing. He toured Wisconsin that summer and even picked up back-to-back wins at Northern Michigan's Gogebic County Fair. The question arose at the end of the summer: would he still be able to keep up this pace at 15?

With his 15th birthday in the books, Derek was one of only two pacers (out of thousands) still racing at that age in the United States.

In June 2015, old Derek Bromac N took his place behind the starting gate once again. Wisconsin's track announcer, George Woodbridge, told the crowd, "In my 50 years of calling races, I've never witnessed a 15-year-old horse racing, and now it is my great honor to introduce you to one of the oldest racing horses in the nation." Woodbridge would have the crowd on their feet with every race; the fans all wanted a good look at the classy old horse dressed in blue, usually with his tongue hanging out.

By late August, time was beginning to take its toll on Derek, as his legs needed constant attention to keep him sound. He showed his love for racing and gave his heart in every race. It was always promised that if he ever didn't have his tongue hanging out while he was on the racetrack, it would be time to hang up the harness. That year's

Gogebic County Fair in Ironwood, Michigan, proved just how much heart the old horse really had. With veteran driver Gary Magee in the sulky, the duo had a solid second place when the lead horse went off stride. Magee remembers, "Derek saw it happen before I did and he just took off. He knew exactly what to do." The crowd was on their feet; the announcer was in a frenzy as Derek won by almost 20 lengths. The horse that was deemed to never race again had just won a race only ticks off the current track record. "We probably could have gone a little faster," Magee smiled, "but we didn't need to." His record-breaking trip to the winner's circle was also his last.

After a few more fairs, the season came to an end.

Derek's heart was ready for his 16-year-old season, but his body had other plans. He had no plans on retiring completely and was put to work as an ambassador for harness racing and the Standardbred breed. In his five years attending Madison, Wisconsin's, Midwest Horse Fair, he educated thousands about the sport of harness racing and the versatility of the breed. He also spent his time hosting clinics, visiting the handicapped and the disabled, and even visiting a few nursing homes. He was always willing to give a ride around the racetrack to anyone who would stop at his barn to say hello. His accomplishments have been featured in multiple newspapers and two issues of Hoof Beats magazine. He was even featured on Wisconsin Public Television's hit show, *Around the Corner with John McGivern*. He participated in parades in his hometown, where he campaigned his latest project, "Reading With a Racehorse," where children wrapped themselves in horse blankets and perched on hay bales as they listened to the story of the well-traveled New Zealand horse. In 2019, he was even deemed the Wisconsin Horse Council's prestigious Equine of the Year Award.

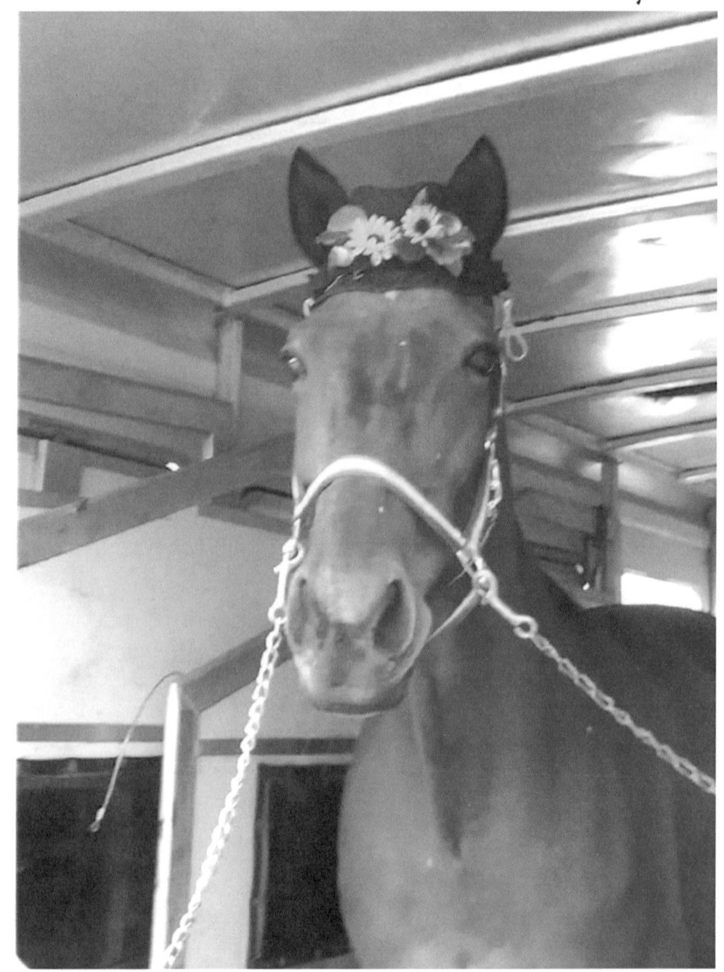

Derek Bromac N has touched so many lives and taught so many people about the sport he dearly loves so much.

About the Author

Amber Sawyer

Hi Y'all! Thanks so much for reading my book. I hope you enjoyed Derek's story as much as I loved sharing it with you. Derek is one amazing animal, and we are so blessed to have him in our lives. My love for horses began at an early age. Every little girl dreams of having a horse. I have lived that dream my entire life. As a little girl, I would ride on my dad's lap on the jog cart as he brought the horses back from the track to the barn. I am a second-generation harness racer. (My son, Paul, is on his way to being the third.) My father was the youngest owner of a racehorse in the entire country at the age of 12 in 1967. His horse's name was Star Heberling. The day he graduated high school, he walked across the stage, picked up his diploma, and headed directly to his pickup to drive from Wisconsin to Pennsylvania. For many years, he pursued his racing career full time at some of the most prestigious racetracks in the country. He came home to Wisconsin to start a family. Neither of my two younger brothers took much of an interest in the horses, so I began driving at the county fairs at the age of 17. Most high schoolers came to school talking about the parties they had gone to over the weekend; I had been at the track. I was often the youngest driver at the races and, more often than not, the only female. I was quickly given the name, "The Pink Lady." My horses were always dressed in as much pink equipment as I could find, and even my helmet and sulky were a bright pink! After graduation, I followed in my father's footsteps and headed to Pennsylvania, working for a trainer with a stable of 75 horses. We trained horses by day, and I spent my nights at the track. I was lucky enough to meet some of the best trainers and drivers in the country! Horsemen often lead a nomadic life, and I was no different. I spent a year in Pennsylvania before moving to Saratoga Springs, New York, and then to Batavia, New York. From there, it was up to Scarborough Downs in Maine.

Maine people are some of the most wonderful people I've ever met. Among my many friends were Peter Kass and his girlfriend, Lauren Grabowlski. We all became very close, but as always, our wandering lifestyles led us on different paths. I moved back to my hometown in Wisconsin and, shortly before my son was born, I received the devastating news that Lauren had been killed in a riding accident. I lost touch with Peter for a while after that, but I heard that he had moved to Ohio and was racing horses at Northfield Park. I was busy raising my son, Paul, and racing at the county fairs in the Midwest.

One day, out of the blue, Peter called me. His favorite horse, Derek Bromac N, had just suffered a very serious suspensory injury to his right front leg. The prognosis from the veterinarian was negative. It was very unlikely that this horse would ever race again. "This horse has the biggest heart of any I've ever seen," Peter said. Would I be willing to take Derek and rehab him? It would be almost a year and half before he would even glance at a racetrack, let alone race on one, if we were lucky. His age was also a factor against him. He was 13! Peter was persistent. "If anyone can get him back to the races, it's you." I was reluctant. A few months of convincing from Peter finally had Derek on a trailer on his way to Wisconsin. A transfer of ownership took place, but no money was exchanged. Derek was a gift.

My son, Paul, was just 8 years old at the time and beginning to show interest in the horses, and Derek's gentle nature made him the perfect first horse for him to learn on.

A year and a half of cold water therapy and a good old-fashioned Wisconsin winter in the snow had Derek healed enough to return to racing.

And the rest is history. Derek began my love for training older horses. I loved their rich history and to learn of their travels. To me, there's a special feeling and a great privilege to take a horse to the track for the final time of their long and distinguished careers, to feel them give their all, and to give them one final look at the grandstand before taking off their harness for the last time.

After Derek's retirement came two other classy horses, Stormin Rustler and Mr. Orchard Street. Both followed in Derek's hoof prints, winning races at 15 and 16, respectively. The combined earnings of those three was a whopping ONE MILLION DOLLARS!

My travels have led me to race horses in Iowa, Wisconsin, Michigan, Illinois, New York, New Jersey, Maryland, New Hampshire, Massachusetts, Maine, Pennsylvania, Ohio, North Dakota, and Minnesota. I have been fortunate enough to race, jog, or train hundreds of horses from first-time starters, to a former Hambletonian contender, a $400,000 winner, and even a former track record holder. My most memorable race was the 4th of July Ladies Race at the oldest racetrack in the country, The Historic Track at Goshen, New York. I don't recall where I finished, but I remember the nostalgic feeling to be a part of the most historical place in harness racing history.

Besides working full time and being a single mother, I am also a freelance writer for *Hoof Beats*, the largest Harness Racing magazine in the country. I also write for the Wisconsin Horseman's News and the Wisconsin Harness Horseman's Association. Derek's story sat on my shelf for a number of years, and now, here it is, finally in your hands! As you read this story, let old Derek be a reminder to you that if you have the heart, no one can tell you what is impossible.

CPSIA information can be obtained
at www.ICGtesting.com
Printed in the USA
LVRC092003160621
690429LV00001B/1